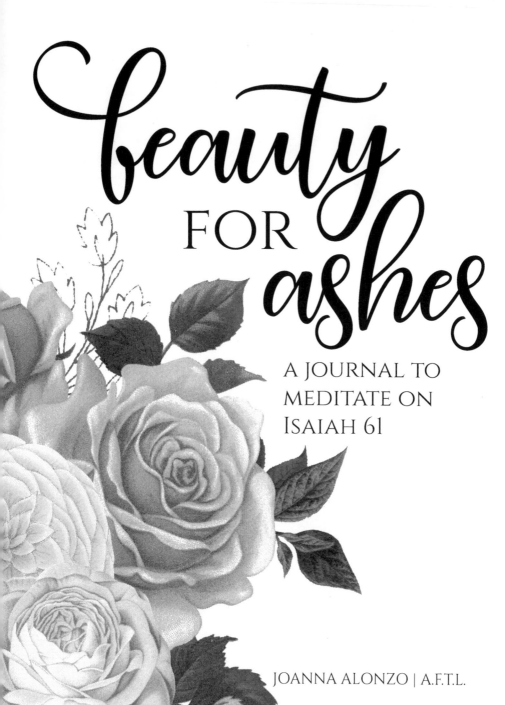

beauty FOR ashes

A JOURNAL TO MEDITATE ON Isaiah 61

JOANNA ALONZO | A.F.T.L.

TO BEBANG

your life's ashes continue
to make many lives — yours
included — much more
beautiful

THE BEAUTY FOR ASHES JOURNAL - #4 Janna Rica
ISBN: 9786218243088

Copyright© 2021 Joanna Alonzo
Published by: Hineni Publishing
Cover and book design by Joanna Alonzo
Content by Joanna Alonzo and other contributors (see back pages)

Scripture taken from the New King James Version®. Copyright © 1982 by
Thomas Nelson. Used by permission. All rights reserved.

Mahal Kita, Pilipinas.

hineni
PUBLISHING

THIS JOURNAL BELONGS TO
THIS *beautiful* one:

THIS JOURNAL IS INSPIRED BY
THE SACRED SCARRED, A CONTEMPORARY
CHRISTIAN RETELLING OF
BEAUTY AND THE BEAST

HEAL THE
frokenhearted

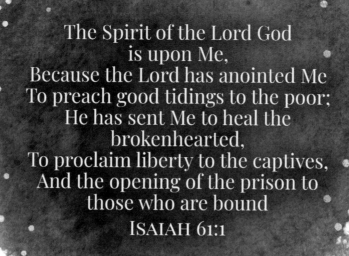

The Spirit of the Lord God
is upon Me,
Because the Lord has anointed Me
To preach good tidings to the poor;
He has sent Me to heal the
brokenhearted,
To proclaim liberty to the captives,
And the opening of the prison to
those who are bound

ISAIAH 61:1

I COOPERATE WITH THE HOLY SPIRIT BY...

The Spirit of the
Lord God
is upon Me

the Lord has
anointed Me

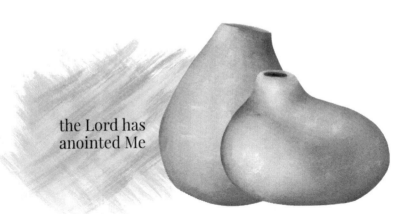

i AM ANOINTED WITH...

WHAT i WILL DO WITH THiS ANOINTING

preach good tidings
to the poor

BLESSED ARE THE POOR
IN SPIRIT, BECAUSE...

_____
_____
_____
_____
_____
_____
_____
_____
_____
_____
_____
_____
_____
_____

THESE ARE THE THINGS
THAT BREAK MY HEART...

He has sent
Me to heal the
brokenhearted

THIS IS WHERE THE HEALING BEGINS.

going deeper

BY: MAY ANN BANG-AY

If I ascend into heaven, You are there;
If I make my bed in hell, behold, You are there. Psalm 139:8

This verse speaks volumes to me. The Lord has vividly and tangibly let me experience Him in the most painful yet most awakening experience I have ever had.

Three years ago, as I sank deeper into my depression, the Lord was there to let me see His glory — not the way I imagined it, but the way He meant it.

The Lord was never vague when He said even when I make my bed in hell, He will be there. Yes, I was making my bed in hell when I heard His voice clearly telling me He loves me, I am sufficient, I am beautiful. While I was indulging myself in the lies of the enemy, the Lord was there sitting with me, listening intently to my woes, seeing, feeling the underlying issues causing my immense loneliness and emptiness. He was there fixing my heart, healing every part of me. Yet, I was fighting him, kicking him, pushing Him away to leave me alone by hurting myself in ways that were unacceptable in His eyes. Yet, His love for me is daring, brave, and reckless. He illustrated this at the cross.

This season of depression broke me and tore me apart, but it also led me to a deeper understanding of who my Saviour is, who my God is, who my Lover is. I was filled with shame and guilt, but God embraced me with His truth, His love, and His grace by showing me who I am in Him. I discovered that knowing Him was the only way to find my true identity.

"HE LOVES ME,
I AM SUFFICIENT,
I AM BEAUTIFUL."

proclaim liberty to
the captives,
and the opening of
the prison to those
who are bound

THESE ARE THE CHAINS
I LONG TO BREAK...

i CLAIM...

wholeheartedness

comfort
ALL WHO MOURN

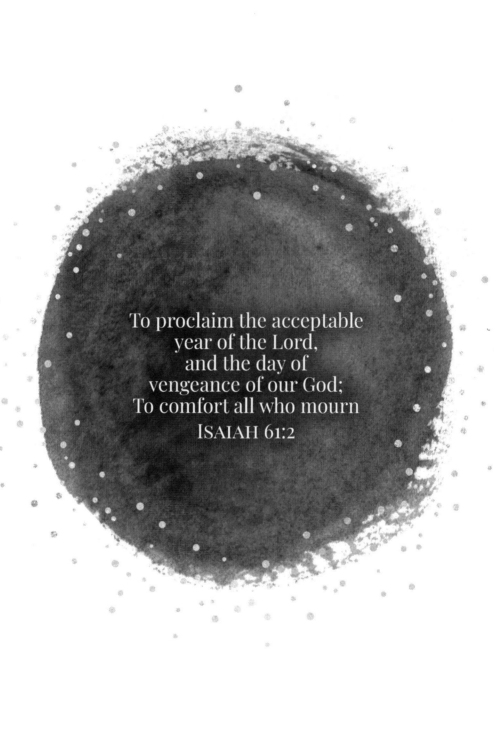

To proclaim the acceptable
year of the Lord,
and the day of
vengeance of our God;
To comfort all who mourn

ISAIAH 61:2

THIS IS THE YEAR TODAY

THIS YEAR IS
A YEAR OF...

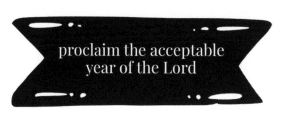

proclaim the acceptable
year of the Lord

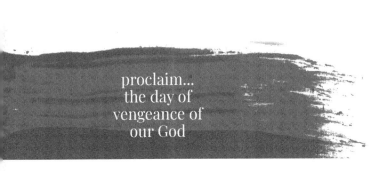

proclaim...
the day of
vengeance of
our God

INJUSTICE

GOD'S PROMISE

WHERE THERE IS INJUSTICE, THERE IS AN
EQUIVALENT PROMISE.

"He bled so we wouldn't have to."

"How do you fall in love with Someone you can't see, Bee? How do you fall in love with God?"

"You first realize His love for you." Bee once again grabbed Calysta's arm and ran her finger over the scars. "There's something about blood that eases the pain and the shame. I used to cut myself as some sort of punishment, almost like an atonement for things I was ashamed of. Or sometimes, I cut myself because I was overwhelmed, and I couldn't explain to anyone what was going on inside me. Does that sound familiar to you?"

"Yeah, I guess." Calysta swallowed hard. Tears brimmed her eyes. "Sometimes, it's like life is punishing me for what my parents did. If I cut myself, then perhaps the pain would be enough to pay for what happened. Like some sort of atonement. If I did it enough, part of me hoped that somehow, I would have my mom back, and I could be as beautiful as my sisters."

Bee's eyes glistened as she gently placed both hands over Calysta's face. "First of all, Calysta, you are fearfully and wonderfully made. Whenever God looks at you, He smiles. You are His masterpiece and you are precious to Him. A Master Artist created you, and you are beautiful. Never doubt that."

A dam broke inside Calysta, and the tears welled up from her eyes. The words struck deep, sounding so good, she would've thought they were lies, but she trusted Bee, whom she couldn't imagine lying.

Bee embraced her and allowed her to sob for the next ten or so minutes. When Calysta pulled away, Bee handed her a box of tissue. As she wiped her tears away, Bee once again looked at the scars on her arm. "You don't have to do this, Calysta. Christ died on the cross so we can escape punishment. He bled so we wouldn't have to. We don't deserve it, because we are sinners and we stumble and we fail, but He did it anyway. Christ was cut, so you wouldn't have to cut yourself. He loves you and He wants to be a part of your life, but you have to let Him in. Do you want to do that?"

AN EXCERPT FROM
CALYSTA AND THE
BEAST, BOOK 1
OF THE SACRED
SCARRED SERIES

GOD IS OUR DEFENDER.
HE AVENGED US AT THE CROSS.

THE BIBLE SAYS THAT GOD
CREATED ME TO BE...

THIS IS THE WAY I DIE TO SELF.

comfort all
who mourn

hope

I SPEAK LIFE TO...

i CLAiM... justice

ACT JUSTLY. LOVE MERCY. WALK HUMBLY.

beauty FOR ASHES

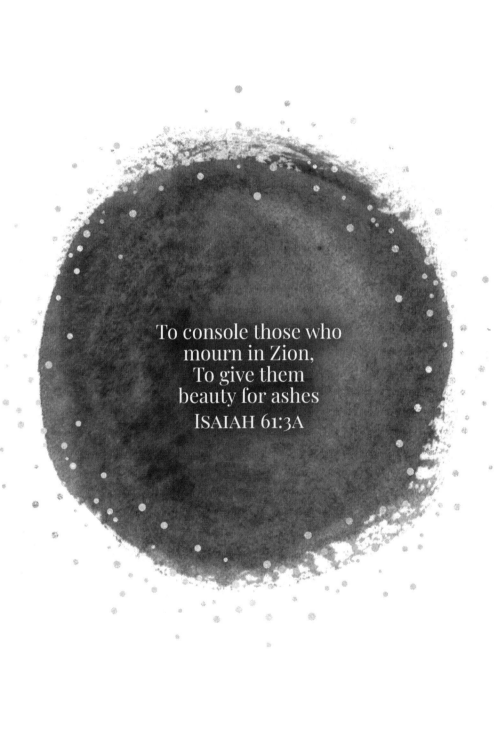

To console those who
mourn in Zion,
To give them
beauty for ashes

ISAIAH 61:3A

my prayer for God's people

_____
_____
_____
_____
_____
_____
_____
_____
_____
_____
_____
_____
_____
_____
_____
_____
_____
_____
_____
_____
_____
_____

console those who mourn in Zion

I WANT TO FIND OR
CREATE BEAUTY HERE...

GOD IS A REFINER.

ashes

beauty

GOD is BEAUTiFUL.

THESE ARE THE PEOPLE WHO MAKE MY LIFE MORE BEAUTIFUL.

beauty for ashes

BY: JANNA RICA ALONZO

He has made everything beautiful in its time. Also He has put eternity in their hearts, except that no one can find out the work that God does from beginning to end. Ecclesiastes 3:11

Eleven years ago, I got in an accident. Our gas tank exploded. My face and my upper and lower extremities got burned. At that time, I didn't know the Lord in a deep, personal way. In the midst of my pain, my mind was filled with questions like, "Does God love me? Does He care?"

As I went through my journey of healing physically, emotionally, and mentally, He gave me the answers to my questions. He was there, every step of the way. He showed Himself to me and who He really is through dreams, visions, and supernatural ways. One incredible miracle was that though my feet and hands have scars, He healed my face totally and left no evidence of the fire. The skin on my face felt and looked like a newborn baby's.

In more ways than one, God assured me: He does love and care for me and everyone else, and to this day, I worship Him for all He has done.

"HE WAS THERE, EVERY STEP OF THE WAY. HE SHOWED HIMSELF TO ME..."

give them
beauty for
ashes

i'm trading my life's ashes
for something beautiful.

i BELIEVE THERE'S BEAUTY HERE.

give them beauty

i CLAIM...
beauty

joy AND praise

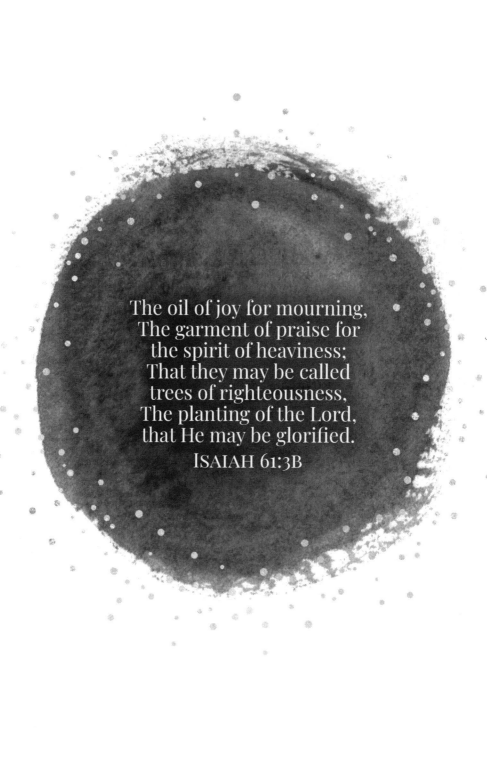

The oil of joy for mourning,
The garment of praise for
the spirit of heaviness;
That they may be called
trees of righteousness,
The planting of the Lord,
that He may be glorified.

ISAIAH 61:3B

THESE ARE THE THINGS
THAT GRIEVE MY HEART...

oil... for
mourning

oil of joy for
mourning

i find joy in...

the garment of
praise for
the spirit of
heaviness

SING to the LORD ALL the earth, proclaim HIS Salvation day after day.

1 Chronicles 26: 23

i PRAISE THE LORD FOR...

Brendan faced the speaker and crossed his arms over his chest. In a matter of minutes, the message captured his attention fully. The guest speaker emphasized purity and honoring God. His message cut through a part of Brendan's heart he hadn't yet dealt with. The girls he had been with. The pain he had caused them. Scarlett's face came to mind. His high school girlfriend. He tried to push the thought away because any recollection of Scarlett brought up years of buried guilt and unbearable shame.

So caught up in both the message and the many ways he had fallen short of this standard of purity God had for His children, Brendan barely comprehended it when the speaker called the worship team on stage.

How was he to go there? To play in front of all these people and worship a God who could see every transgression he had ever committed?

"Brendan, come on." Devon tapped his shoulder.

Reluctantly, Brendan stood up and walked to the stage. He sat on his spot behind the keyboard and watched for Devon's signal to start. *God, You cover all sins. Cover mine. Make me holy as You are holy.* Brendan played the first key and the moment he did, goosebumps filled his body. God's presence descended upon them and permeated every corner of that sanctuary. He saturated Brendan's soul and spirit, and even as he continued to worship God with his skill and talent, he learned to worship God with all his heart, soul, strength, and mind. Brendan trembled as he yet again experienced God's presence manifested. Cries of a people desperate for God filled the hall, and Brendan got swept away in it all.

"...EVEN AS HE CONTINUED TO WORSHIP GOD WITH HIS SKILL AND TALENT, HE LEARNED TO WORSHIP GOD WITH ALL HIS HEART, SOUL, STRENGTH, AND MIND."

AN EXCERPT FROM BEAUTY AND THE BRUTE, BOOK 2 OF THE SACRED SCARRED SERIES

WRITE DOWN THE LYRICS OF THE SONG OF YOUR HEART IN THIS SEASON.

GOD IS MY RIGHTEOUSNESS.

they may be called
trees of
righteousness

the planting of the Lord,
that He may be glorified

THESE ARE THE
WAYS i CAN
GLORIFY GOD TODAY.

i CLAIM...
joy

rebuild AND restore

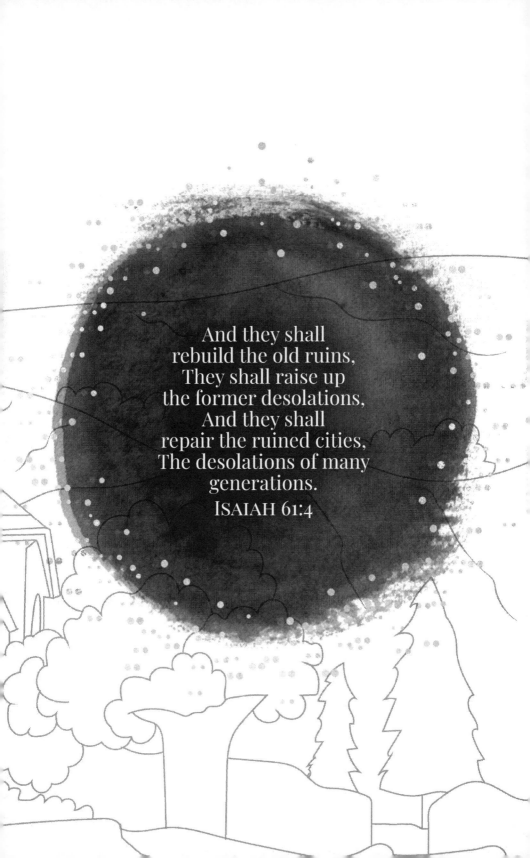

And they shall
rebuild the old ruins,
They shall raise up
the former desolations,
And they shall
repair the ruined cities,
The desolations of many
generations.

ISAIAH 61:4

they shall
rebuild the old
ruins

I PRAY FOR THE REPAIR AND RESTORATION OF
THESE BROKEN RELATIONSHIPS...

TO THOSE WHO DARE

To those who dare
To start small
But dream big
To be vulnerable
In spite of the scars

To love again
To keep breathing
To forgive
And yes... to forget
To embrace life
And take risks
To stare down the
impossible
And say, "It can be done"

To those who dare
To smile
And say, "Thank you"
Even if they're struggling
Even if they're hurt

To cry
To seek for help
To admit their weakness
To trust

To let others shine
To be humble and selfless
To play second fiddle
To put others first

To those who dare
To know when to say "No"
And say it
To stand for what's right
To be wise

To laugh
At themselves
At their problems
At their own jokes

To face their fears
To get out of their comfort
zones
To overcome
To never give up

To those who dare
To learn
To admit fault
To stand up
When they fall

To believe
To hope
To love
Extravagantly

To those who dare
Thank you
Because of you, I can dare too

dedicated to: Nhof, for
being brave enough to be
vulnerable

THIS iS WHAT iNSPiRES ME...

arise!

they shall
raise up
the former
desolations

they shall
repair the ruined
cities

LORD, RAISE UP A STANDARD OF RIGHTEOUSNESS FOR OUR CITY.

REBUILD THESE BROKEN AREAS, GOD.

repair... the desolations
of many generations

GOD, REDEEM &
RECONCILE THESE
GENERATIONS.

i CLAIM...

restoration

favor
WITH GOD
AND MAN

Strangers shall stand and
feed your flocks,
And the sons of the foreigner
Shall be your plowmen and your
vinedressers.

ISAIAH 61:5

strangers
shall stand
and feed
your flocks

_____

_____

_____

_____

_____

_____

_____

_____

_____

_____

_____

_____

_____

_____

THIS IS A STORY OF A STRANGER WHO
WAS KIND TO ME.

THESE PEOPLE HAVE BEEN
A BLESSING TO ME. BLESS
THEM, LORD.

favor

THESE ARE THE WAYS GOD HAS SHOWN ME FAVOR.

AS AN INHERITANCE, i
PRAY FOR THE NATIONS OF...

"I meant we should stay here. In the island. Longer."

At what he said, a shot of excitement coursed through her system. She rested her chin on his chest.

Brendan had his eyes closed, a satisfied smile on his face.

"Are you serious?" Calysta dared to ask. He made it hard to tell.

"I know Adam and Bee are expecting you back in Thailand, but they did say at our wedding that we can take all the time we need to decide on our future. They understand our dynamic is different now that we're married. If anything, they would probably be thrilled for us if we tell them we want to extend our stay here and get involved with Cardo and Santana's church."

"Brendan, I—" Calysta couldn't believe her ears. "Wait. What are you saying?" Without thinking it through, she sat up on the hammock. The sudden motion caused the contraption to shake, which made Brendan jolt where he lay, throwing off the balance. The hammock flipped and threw both of them to the ground. Upon hitting the sand, Calysta burst out laughing.

Meanwhile, Brendan was busy checking if she was okay.

"I'm fine, I'm fine." Calysta dusted off sand from her dress. "I guess it's time for us to take a walk, because love, you're talking crazy, and I'm loving every minute of it."

Brendan's face lit up. "You mean you'd consider it? I know it's not what we planned to do, but it feels right. It's not like we'll live here permanently. Just for a season, and—"

"Brendan—" Calysta knelt up and cupped his cheeks between her hands "—you're speaking my language. All this time, I thought you wanted to return to New York right after. Especially with everything going on with your family and your mother's company. I didn't even think returning to Thailand was an option."

Surprise extended the angles of his face as he creased his brows to take in what she was saying. "But what about Adam and Bee?"

"You said so yourself, they understand that things are different now that I'm your wife."

He grinned. "Still loving the sound of that."

Calysta nodded. "Me too."

He leaned over to kiss her, and in that fraction of eternity, everything seemed possible. Their decision to extend their stay gave them the understanding that nothing was holding them back from pursuing whatever God was calling them to do.

AN EXCERPT FROM
BRENDAN AND THE BELLE, BOOK 3 OF
THE SACRED SCARRED SERIES

FATHER, iF i HAVE FOUND FAVOR iN YOUR EYES, PLEASE GRANT ME THiS...

your plowmen and
your vinedressers

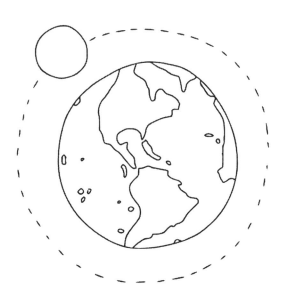

MAY THE WEALTH OF THE NATIONS
COME INTO YOUR KINGDOM, LORD.

the sons of
the foreigner
shall be your
plowmen and
vinedressers

i CLAIM...
abundance

servants
OF OUR GOD

But you shall be named
the priests of the Lord,
They shall call you
the servants of our God.
You shall eat the riches
of the Gentiles,
And in their glory
you shall boast.

ISAIAH 61:6

you shall be
named
the priests of
the Lord

MAKE ME HOLY AS YOU ARE HOLY, LORD.

why i do what i do

BY: RHEMA GRACE AKISTAL

And you shall love the Lord your God with all your heart, with all your soul, with all your mind, and with all your strength.' This is the first commandment. And the second, like it, is this: 'You shall love your neighbor as yourself.' There is no other commandment greater than these. Mark 12:30-31, NKJV

Being a pastor's kid, I began to serve the Lord at a young age. My parents were both in ministry and missions before they even met, and continued to serve God even while married. Once my mom recognized I could already understand spiritual things, she personally and continually preached the Gospel to me. She prayed for me.

One time, our family went to a birthday celebration of a church member. Dad was preaching about "When a man be born once, he would die twice. But if a man be born twice, he would die once." This would be the Lord's final knock at the door of my heart. At almost twelve, I understood who God really was to me. I was born again in the spirit. By then, I got to have this new real relationship with God. It was the start of my journey with Him, to know that I no longer live myself but for Him willingly, lovingly, and unconditionally gave His life for me. I started not just to read but to meditate on the Word of God, the Bible. I started not just to thank the Lord for the food we eat but to talk to Him like I talk to a person. These may be my small beginnings and just basic Christian living but these were the very solid foundations that grew my faith in God even until now. Through these basic, but most significant, things in a Christian life, I grew to know God personally and to love God all the more.

So why do I do what I do? My answer is no other than His unconditional love for me, His arms wide open ready to embrace me, and His free gift of eternal life. As I grew in the Lord, Mark 12:30-31 became a revelation in me as to why I live on, and what's my purpose in life.

> "AT ALMOST TWELVE, I UNDERSTOOD WHO GOD REALLY WAS TO ME."

they shall
call you
the servants
of our God

you shall eat
the riches
of the Gentiles

HE PREPARES A
TABLE FOR ME.
WHAT IS IN IT?

i AM HUNGRY FOR...

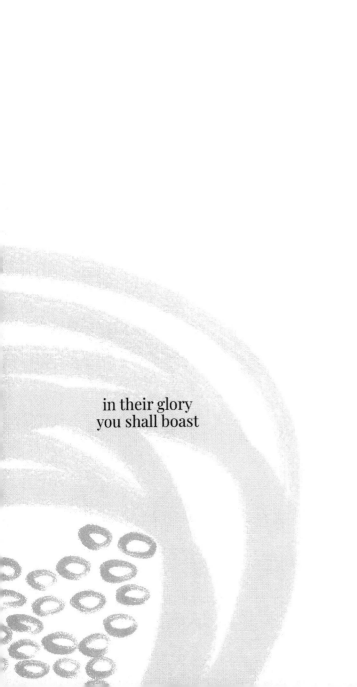

in their glory
you shall boast

SHOW ME NOW YOUR *glory*

i CLAIM...
dignity

double honor
FOR SHAME

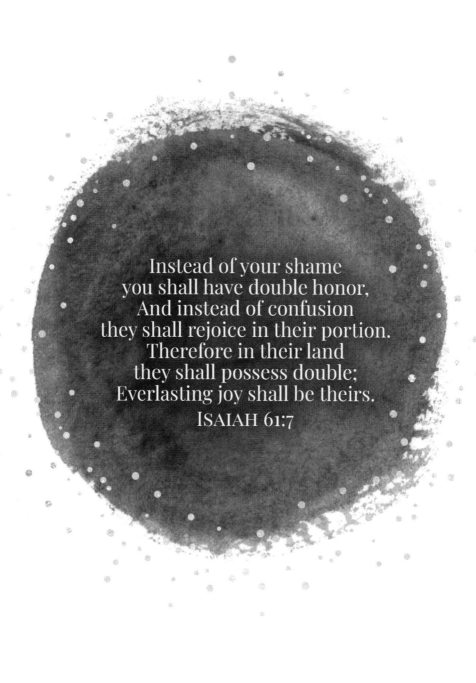

Instead of your shame
you shall have double honor,
And instead of confusion
they shall rejoice in their portion.
Therefore in their land
they shall possess double;
Everlasting joy shall be theirs.

ISAIAH 61:7

instead of
your shame

THESE ARE THE WAYS GOD FREED ME FROM SHAME...

THESE ARE THE WAYS GOD
HONORS THE RIGHTEOUS...

you shall have
double honor

Then he said it: a promise spoken with determination and clear intent. "You belong with me, Calysta. Someday, you'll see."

Not giving her a chance to respond, he gave her a curt nod, turned around, and returned to his family. His new girl gave him a peck on the cheek. Calysta's eyes lingered on them. How could he say what he said, walk away, and then hold her like nothing happened? Calysta knew then how wrong Lance was. He would always be one of her dearest, most beloved friends, but no, she didn't belong with him.

"Calysta!" Malaya threw her arms around her from the back. "We made it!"

Calysta laughed as she spun around to hug her best friend back. "We did!"

To her surprise, tears were flowing down Malaya's face. "I will miss you. I will miss us."

Suddenly, the reality of goodbye hit Calysta. Malaya was traveling across the country to another state. Lance was off to university. Meanwhile, Calysta still hadn't decided what to do.

She tried to enjoy the rest of the time she had with her friends and classmates, but before she went to bed that evening, she got on her knees, and in tears, asked God to show her His plans and His will for her life.

He didn't answer. God chose to be silent when she wanted His voice, distant when she wanted His embrace, patient when she wanted His urgency. And all she could do was wait, trust, and hold on to peace incomprehensible — a peace that would guide her way.

"...ALL SHE COULD DO WAS WAIT, TRUST, AND HOLD ON TO PEACE INCOMPREHENSIBLE — A PEACE THAT WOULD GUIDE HER WAY."

AN EXCERPT FROM CALYSTA AND THE BEAST, BOOK 1 OF THE SACRED SCARRED SERIES

A sense with

instead of confusion

they shall
rejoice in
their portion

THIS is MY
PORTiON...

MAY GOD ESTABLISH MY
LIFE IN THESE AREAS...

in their land
they shall possess
double

everlasting joy
shall be theirs

TO HAVE
EVERLASTING JOY
IS TO HAVE...

i CLAiM...
double

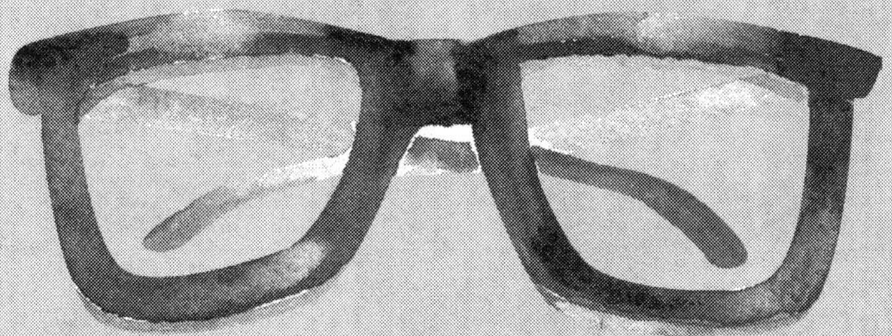

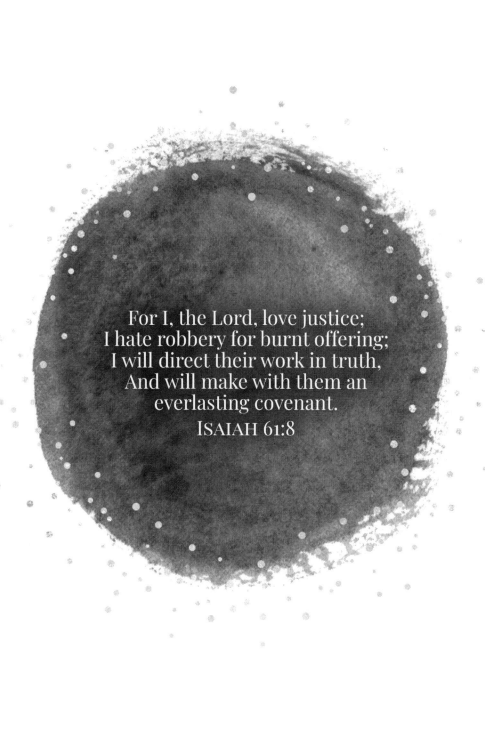

For I, the Lord, love justice;
I hate robbery for burnt offering;
I will direct their work in truth,
And will make with them an
everlasting covenant.

ISAIAH 61:8

I, the Lord, love justice

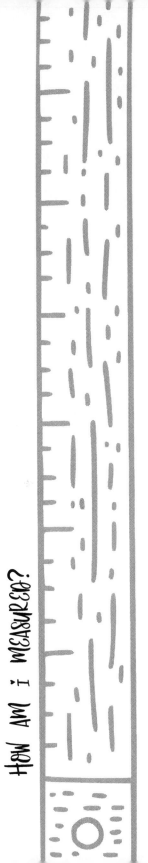

HOW AM I MEASURED?

i'M TAKiNG BACK
WHAT THE ENEMY HAS
STOLEN FROM ME!

The Healer and the Beast

I do not serve a blind God. Your eyes are wide open.
Always searching, forever seeing, eternally knowing.
Ever present, you were there. You were watching my fight.
You stood witness as I succumbed to the cold, harsh blow
That made me give up on winning this battle inside.

I ran. I fled. I wallowed in the darkness of my retreat.
Away from you. Away from the light.
I licked my wounds like a beast damned for eternity.
Shameful, lonesome, wretched, ravenous beast.
A stark contrast to the blissful glory of life in your hands.

I made the world my momentary tourniquet.
I bundled myself in its controlling, murderous grasp.
Reveling in the numbness and the pressure,
Living out of the illusion that I could last without my source of life.
Living without my source of life. What a fool I was.

But I do not serve a blind God. Your eyes are wide open.
You saw the struggle. You saw the fall.
You saw the aching, bleeding heart
That rejected this world as its momentary tourniquet.
And in your gentle, healing way, you tore this heart away.

Bleeding apart from the useless rags I thought would heal,
I once again look unto your light.
Though the pain remains and the blood flows,
I do not serve a blind God. Your eyes are wide open.
Your light is the one healing tourniquet that will bring me back to life.

I hate
robbery
for burnt
offering

i CANNOT GIVE GOD
WHAT ISN'T MINE.

I NEED HIS
DIRECTION IN...

I will direct their
work in truth

I will make with
them an everlasting
covenant

COVENANTS i HAVE
MADE WITH THE LORD.

AM I SOWING
TOWARD ETERNITY?

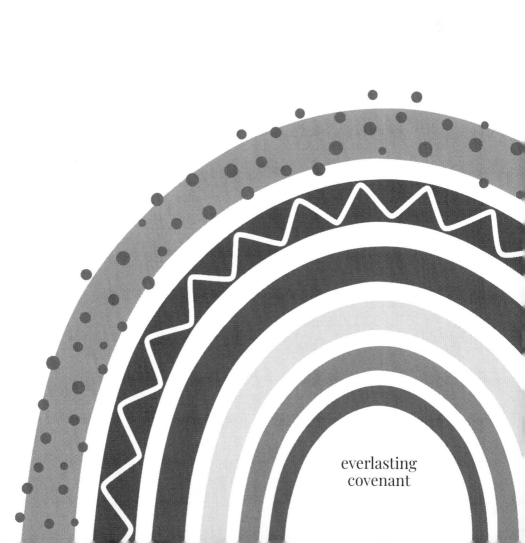

everlasting
covenant

i CLAiM...
truth

Legacy & Longevity

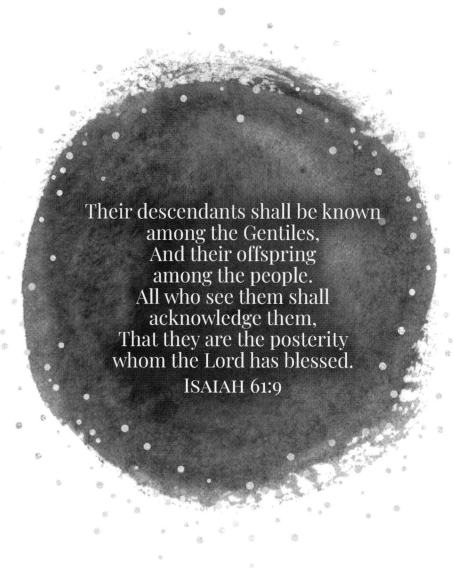

Their descendants shall be known
among the Gentiles,
And their offspring
among the people.
All who see them shall
acknowledge them,
That they are the posterity
whom the Lord has blessed.

ISAIAH 61:9

Their
descendants
shall be known
among the
Gentiles

i BELONG TO THiS GENERATION...

☐ GEN ALPHA
(born 2013–2025)

☐ GEN Z
(born 1997–2012)

☐ MILLENNIALS
(born 1981–1996)

☐ GEN X
(born 1965–1980)

☐ BOOMERS 2
(born 1955–1964)

☐ BOOMERS 1
(born 1946–1954)

☐ POST WAR
(born 1928–1945)

Their
descendants
shall be
known

Blessed

their
offspring
among the
people

i PRAY FOR MY SPIRITUAL CHILDREN, NAMELY:

HOW i HONOR AND ACKNOWLEDGE MY SPIRITUAL PARENTS

"She kicked me out."

Mateo winced. "And you just went home?"

"What was I supposed to do? She didn't want me around!"

"I would've stuck it out, man."

Brendan tensed. The idea that he had yet again failed Calysta somehow hit him hard. "Well, I'm not you, am I?"

Mateo brushed his palm against Sab's back. "Don't worry about it. I'm sure she'll be fine. Emotions are high right now, and everyone's on edge. I'll go check on Paige and Calysta."

Brendan thought of going with him, but he couldn't stand Calysta shooing him away again, so he stayed.

Emilia stood by Karina's bed and brushed a hand on Karina's forehead. His aunt closed her eyes and prayed in silence.

Brendan stared at Karina's motionless form. He felt nothing other than exhaustion and frustration at all the antics she had pulled since he had arrived. As if he and Calysta didn't already have enough problems to deal with in their relationship, Karina had to complicate everything.

Emilia's phone rang. She fished it out of her purse and cringed when she saw who was calling. "It's Kirk. I need to take this."

Brendan shrugged it off. Yet another thing going on in his life he couldn't understand or control.

Emilia walked out of the room as she answered, "Hello?"

And so there they were. Just him and unconscious Karina.

"At least you're a lot quieter this way," he muttered under his breath. He caught himself realizing how erratic his emotions were toward the troubled young woman. Irritation, frustration, annoyance, pity, sympathy, empathy, anger, and then finally, nothing. Nothing but this callousness toward her plight.

Brendan shut his eyes and uttered a prayer. *God, I don't know who else to go to. Forgive me for my selfishness, Lord. You understand why I am frustrated with this person, but I know You care about her much more than any of us do. Whatever's happening, bring healing in this place. For her. And for all of us as well. Help me see her the way You see her and have for her the same heart You have for us. I hope that makes sense. I don't know what I'm saying here, but Lord, You understand. All this I pray, in Your Holy Name—* He opened his eyes and said out loud, "Amen."

The moment the word left his mouth, Karina's hand twitched and in a few seconds, her eyes flickered open.

AN EXCERPT FROM
BEAUTY AND THE BRUTE, BOOK 2 OF
THE SACRED SCARRED SERIES

All who see them shall acknowledge them,

LORD, MAY WE BE A BLESSING
THROUGHOUT GENERATIONS.

Happy Day

they are the
posterity
whom the Lord
has blessed

THE LORD HAS
BLESSED US WITH...

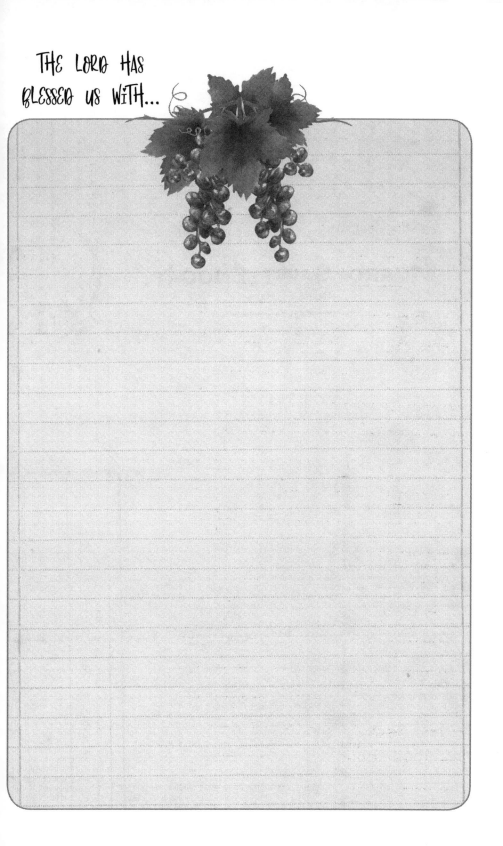

i CLAiM...
inheritance

THE *bride*

I will greatly rejoice in the Lord,
My soul shall be joyful in my God;
For He has clothed me with
the garments of salvation,
He has covered me with
the robe of righteousness,
As a bridegroom decks himself
with ornaments,
And as a bride adorns herself
with her jewels.

ISAIAH 61:10

|||| ||||
||||

LET'S COUNT THE
REASONS TO REJOICE

I will greatly rejoice in the Lord

My soul shall
be joyful in
my God

MY SOUL DELIGHTS
IN GOD, BECAUSE...

from broken to whole

BY: MAILA REANO

I grew up in Sunday school and have been going to church since I was young. All that time, I thought knowing the Name of Jesus is enough. However, it was when I got married and eventually migrated to Dubai, UAE that my relationship with Jesus was put to the test.

My husband and I had a good start in Dubai. Having a good job and financial freedom, we enjoyed every chance we could get to party, hang out with friends, and so on. I got caught up in all the trends and lifestyles perpetuated by my peers. Our collection of various plastic cards grew, swiping for whatever we liked, so we can stay on trend.

In 2006, our firstborn, Danielle, was born around the time my husband lost his job. Our finances slowly sank, and it became a challenge to pay off my credit. We had to move from our two-bedroom flat to a single-room shared villa. More and more, we failed to pay our bills and began to receive threatening calls from bank collection agents.

The sleepless nights followed. Focusing on work became a challenge because of constant calls on my phone. It was humiliating even as I scrounged for money to borrow from friends and coworkers. My circle of friends dwindled. I felt abandoned and lost. Constant arguing at home turned my marriage into a nightmare.

Bitterness, confusion, and regret led me to a place of brokenness, and I began to seek God in church. There, I discovered the pieces I needed to rebuild. Jesus rescued and restored me by His love and grace. My husband and I both committed to serve the Lord and surrender all our problems to Him. From that point on, God moved us from broken to whole. He provided various ways for us to repay our debts and once again get financial freedom. He bestowed upon us a crown of beauty instead of ashes. He can certainly do the same thing for you!

Today, Maila and Rey Reano are head pastors at Ebenezer Ministry, pioneering a church in Dubai, which they envision as a catalyst of His gospel to reach all races and nationalities for God's glory!

He has clothed me with
the garments of salvation

He has
covered me
with
the robe of
righteousness

IT IS GOD WHO
MAKES ME RIGHTEOUS

i WiLL PREPARE...

As a bridegroom decks
himself with ornaments

as a bride adorns
herself
with her jewels

i WILL GET READY.

i CLAIM...
love

HIS PEOPLE WILL *flourish*

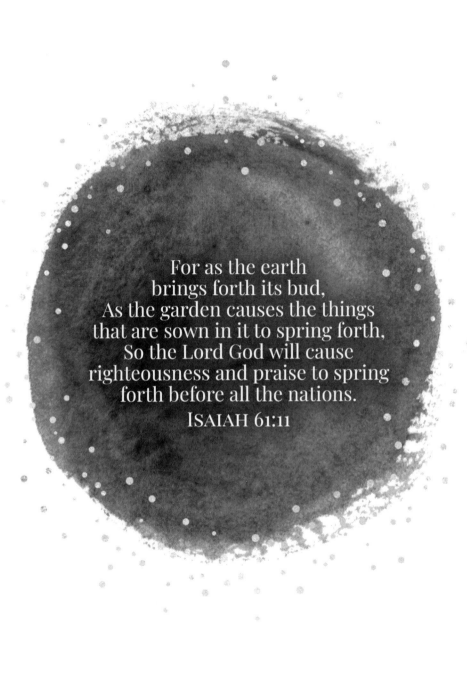

For as the earth
brings forth its bud,
As the garden causes the things
that are sown in it to spring forth,
So the Lord God will cause
righteousness and praise to spring
forth before all the nations.

ISAIAH 61:11

as the earth
brings forth its bud

the garden causes the
things that are sown in it to
spring forth

i EXPECT TO REAP...

THIS IS HOW GOD
HAS BEEN WORKING
IN MY LIFE.

the Lord God
will cause
righteousness

GOD CAUSES
RIGHTEOUSNESS BY...

GOD IS WORTHY OF PRAISE, BECAUSE...

the Lord God
will cause...
praise

"Psst! Psst! Psst!" The boy mimicked him and flexed his arms to reveal his non-existent muscles. "Strong!"

"That's right!" Brendan grinned. "You're strong!"

Truth be told, Brendan didn't mind taking the attention from Santana and her children. He enjoyed making the kids laugh, but more than anything, he loved seeing Calysta surrounded by children. She was such a natural with them.

Even in that moment, the girls in the village surrounded her, caressing her hair and telling her how *maganda* — beautiful — they thought she was. Somehow, around him, children were rambunctious and full of energy. With Calysta, they were calm and at rest, almost like they're lost in wonder.

As Brendan tried to keep up with the boys in the village, he stole glances at his wife, reminded of that moment on their first day at Isla Blanca when he noticed a similarity in countenance between Calysta and Santana. It was only when Cardo called in the children to give the couple a reprieve that Brendan pegged what it was about them that attracted him. It was the same thing that drew him to Belle on his eighteenth birthday.

When Calysta approached him, it felt to him like déjà vu, because it reminded him of the first time he had seen Belle. There was an ethereal quality about Calysta that had grown more clear the more she followed hard after God. Brendan realized he had seen glimpses of it in many people before — in Belle, in Cardo and Santana, in Adam and Bee, in Mateo and Paige, in Emilia, in Luke and Scarlett, in so many people who had influenced their lives. It was the Spirit of God in them, manifested through a season of fullness.

Calysta was radiant, and every time she caught his eye, she took his breath away.

AN EXCERPT FROM
BRENDAN AND THE
BELLE, BOOK 3 OF
THE SACRED SCARRED
SERIES

I LONG TO SEE THE SALVATION OF THESE NATIONS.

i CLAIM...

a harvest of...

THiS ENDS THiS JOURNAL.

BY SIMPLY OWNING THIS JOURNAL, YOU HAVE BEEN A BLESSING.

We pray that this journal has blessed you and that it has helped you explore the truths of Isaiah 61 in a deeper way. May it be a catalyst for you to dive deeper into meditating on His Word and finding how personal it can be even as it expands your heart and mind to see beyond yourself.

We are living in extreme times, and we may unfortunately see more than our fair share of ashes in this world, but we can always trust God to be true to His Word.

Isaiah 61 says that Jesus came to give beauty for ashes. When all is said and done, all will be beautiful again.

May you continue to be blessed and be a blessing!

Also, if possible, we would appreciate it if you post a review of this journal on Amazon, Shopee, or your social media sites. It will be of great help to us!

Salamat and shalom to you!

Joanna Alonzo

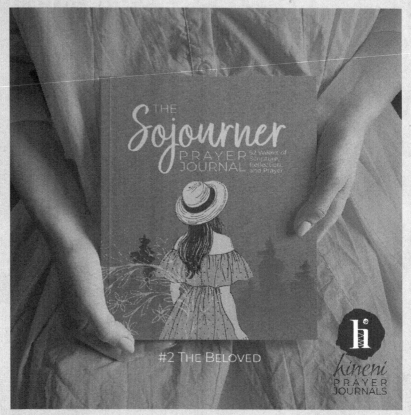

#2 THE BELOVED

If you like this journal, you may want to check out other journals by *Hineni Publishing*. You can find out more about what other journals we have available at **www.hinenipublishing.com**.

contributors

Thank you to these lovely women who graciously shared their stories with us on how God has given them beauty for ashes!

MAILA REANO
(with husband, Rey)
From Broken to Whole

ANNE BANG-AY
Going Deeper

RHEMA GRACE AKISTAL
Why I Do What I Do

JANNA RICA ALONZO
Beauty for Ashes

If you are interested in sharing your writing — whether a testimony, piece of poetry, essay, or short story — please message us at *contributors@hinenipublishing.com* for more information on what type of writing we are looking for.

about the author

Joanna Alonzo is a Filipina with no permanent address, but no, she's not homeless. She loves calling herself a walking paradox, because like most people, she can be quite a moving mass of contradictions (e.g. wandering homebody, beautiful mess, etc.) She is intrigued by the world and its people, who day by day, continue to convince her that God is the greatest Storyteller of all. Find out more about her and her work at **www.joannaalonzo.com**.

about the publisher

Hineni (יננה) is a Hebrew word that means "Here am I" or "Here I am". It's how Abraham, Moses, Samuel, and Isaiah responded to the voice of the Lord when He called on them. It denotes not a presentation of ourselves as ready and totally available.

Hineni Publishing is a Philippine-based Christian company established in 2020. The heart and vision of Hineni Publishing is to produce books and literature written by "a ready scribe" seeking to please the King as in Psalm 45:1 - "My heart overflows with a pleasing theme; I address my verses to the king; my tongue isw like the pen of a ready scribe." (ESV)

 hinenipublishing

AND LET THE BEAUTY OF THE LORD OUR GOD BE UPON US,
AND ESTABLISH THE WORK OF OUR HANDS FOR US;
YES, ESTABLISH THE WORK OF OUR HANDS.
PSALM 90:17

Made in the USA
Monee, IL
16 August 2023

41122841R00111